Come for a S

Story by Joy Cowley

"Mom! Dad! Come for a swim!"
the children called.

2

"Coming!" said Dad,
and he ran into the water.

"Coming!" said Mom, and
she put on her suntan oil.

4

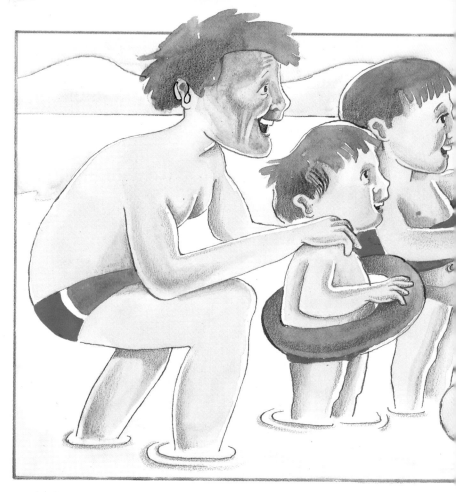

"Come on, Mom!" they called.

"Coming!" said Mom,
and she lay on the towel.

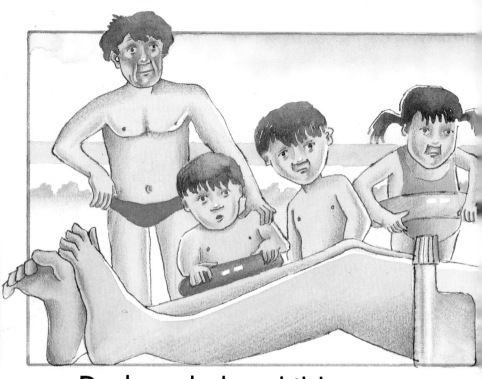

Dad and the children
were waiting.
They called to Mom,
"Why don't you come in
for a swim?"

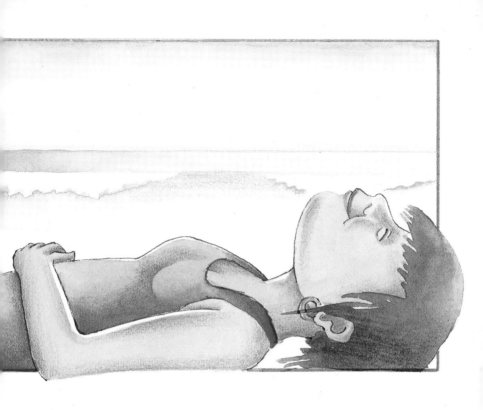

"I am coming," said Mom,
and she shut her eyes.

Dad got a bucket.
He filled it with water.

He dumped the water
over Mom.
Mom yelled.

Mom ran after Dad.
"You wait!" she yelled.
"I'll get you!"

Dad ran into the water.
Mom ran after him.

Mom and Dad
splashed each other.

They fell over
and laughed and laughed.

Then Mom and Dad
and the children
had a swim.